Guitar Basics Repertoire

Fun solos and ensemble pieces for individual and group learning

James Longworth and Nick Walker

Illustrations by Andy Cooke

FABER *ff* MUSIC

track

1

Tuning
track

Teachers' parts and backing tracks

Teachers' parts and backing tracks for many of the pieces in this book are provided on the CD.

Acknowledgements

For Eve, Cristian and Anna. Thanks to Carolina and Masha for their patience and support. Thanks also to Fiona Bolton, Leigh Rumsey and all at Faber Music for their belief in the idea and support to bring it to fruition.

Unless otherwise stated, all musical content is by James Longworth and Nick Walker

© 2010 by Faber Music Ltd
This edition © 2012 by Faber Music Ltd
Bloomsbury House
74–77 Great Russell Street
London WC1B 3DA
Music processed by MusicSet 2000
Illustrations by Andy Cooke
Design by Susan Clarke
Printed in England by Caligraving Ltd
All rights reserved

ISBN10: 0-571-53687-5
ISBN13: 978-0-571-53687-0

To buy Faber Music publications or to find out about the full range of titles available please contact your local retailer or Faber Music sales enquiries:

Faber Music Limited, Burnt Mill, Elizabeth Way, Harlow CM20 2HX England
Tel: +44 (0) 1279 82 89 82   Fax: +44 (0) 1279 82 89 83
sales@fabermusic.com   fabermusic.com

Welcome to Guitar Basics Repertoire!

In this book you'll find lots of new songs (and some familiar ones) which you can play either with your teacher or friends. Some songs have been written so that you can play them on your own as solo pieces, which is great practice if you are thinking of taking graded exams.

We hope that you have lots of fun developing your playing with these pieces.

James and Nick

contents

unit 1 Fast and smooth

These pieces will help you to develop fluency and speed using the notes you learnt in *Guitar Basics*. The first piece uses your right-hand fingers and the second, your thumb; played together they create a cat and mouse duet.

track 2 The Cat's Whiskers

track 2 Mousetrap

note reminder

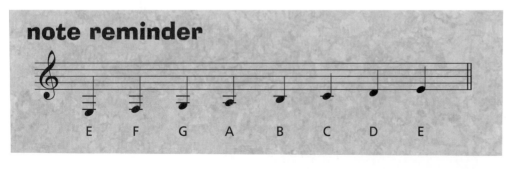

Aura Lee

Track 3

This American folk song was made famous by Elvis Presley in the 1950s when he put new words to the traditional melody.

Ask a friend to strum the chords whilst you play the melody to create a duet, then swap parts.

The next song is from the Caribbean and uses rhythms you learnt in *Guitar Basics*. Tap this phrase before you play the song to remind yourself how to count dotted and syncopated rhythms.

Stretch the beat and get up and dance.

Brown Girl in the Ring

Track 4

fact file

This song doesn't start on the first beat of the bar. Count '1-2-3' at the speed of the piece and start playing on beat 4. This is called an **upbeat**.

These pieces use extended techniques to change the sound of the guitar. (You may remember the first piece from *Guitar Basics*.)

track 5 The Soldier's March

To start this piece, make the sound of a marching drum by flipping string 5 over string 6 and pressing them down at the 10th fret. Strike the strings with your thumb and repeat this rhythm, gradually getting louder.

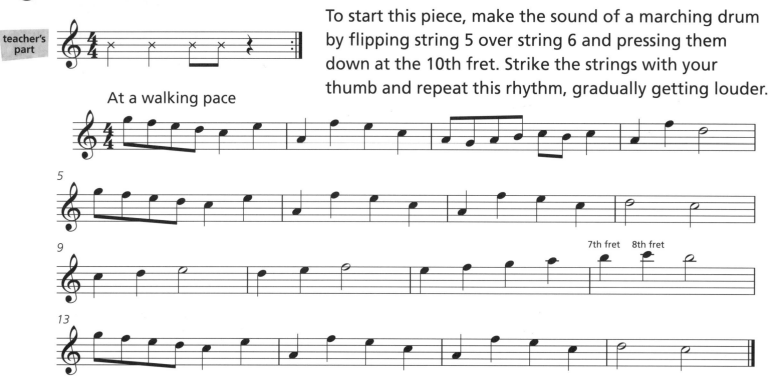

To finish the piece, use the drum rhythm to create the impression that the soldiers are marching away.

track 6 March of the Kings

Play this phrase as an introduction, muting the sound with your right palm by lightly touching the strings just in front of the bridge. This effect is called **pizzicato** (or pizz.).

Bizet

Slip 'n' Slide

It is possible to play the same note on several different strings. In this piece E is
sometimes played at the 5th fret on the B string (instead of the open E string),
and B is sometimes played at the 4th fret on the G string (instead of the open B string).

When you see this sign ╱ slide your finger up to the note.

Can you find any other places you could create a slippery sound by sliding up to the note?

Smoke Signals

The unusual noteheads ◇ are harmonics. To play these, touch the E string directly
above fret 12 as lightly as you can. Strum the top three strings when you see ⬆.

unit 2 Accidentals and key signatures

In *Guitar Basics* you learnt that a sharpened note (♯) is played one fret higher than a natural. Remember that a sharp sign applies until the end of the bar unless a natural sign (♮) cancels it. Look out for the upbeats at the start of each piece.

More Sore Fingers

fact file

Fernando Sor and Ferdinando Carulli were two of the most important guitarists and composers of the early 19th century. The Italian term **andante** means 'at a walking pace'.

Andante

fact file

A **flat** (♭) lowers the pitch of a note by one fret and, like a sharp, applies until the end of the bar unless cancelled out by a natural sign.

Remember you can play E on the B string (see page 7). E♭ is located one fret lower at the 4th fret.

Similarly you can play B on the G string. B♭ is positioned one fret lower at the 3rd fret.

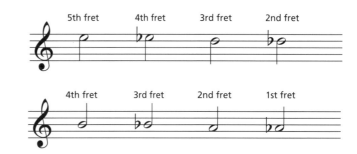

Flat Attack

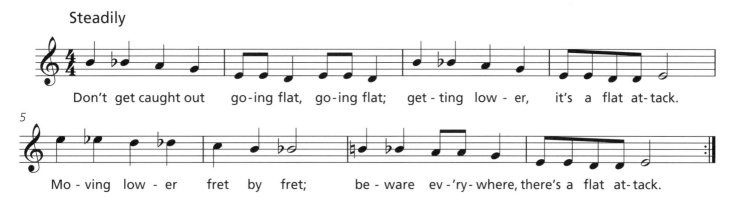

Don't get caught out   go-ing flat, go-ing flat;   get-ting low-er,   it's a flat at-tack.

Mo-ving low-er   fret by fret;   be-ware ev-'ry-where, there's a flat at-tack.

Nightwatch

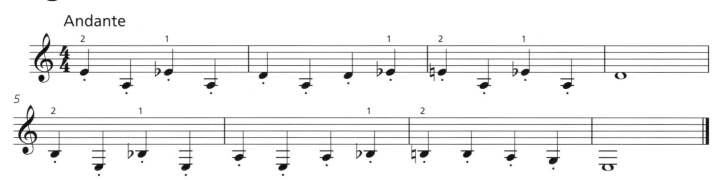

Spooky

This melody can be played together with the piece of the same eery title on page 12 of *Guitar Basics*.

track 9 Blue Boogaloo

Swung

track 10 Bear Hunt

He's a Pirate   from 'Pirates of the Caribbean'

Words and Music by Klaus Badelt, Hans Zimmer and Geoffrey Zanelli

fact file

*Sharps and flats can be written at the beginning of a piece. This is called a **key signature**.*

Play this scale to get used to playing in the key of G.
How many F♯s can you find in this exercise?

Now try this short tune. Don't forget the F♯s! Ask your teacher
to play the chords to accompany your melody, then swap parts.

⑪ Homeward Bound

Relaxing

Minuet in G

Stately

J. S. Bach

Lame Horse Blues

Blue Bear's Bass

This piece can be played together with
Big Blue Bear on page 7 of *Guitar Basics*.

unit 3 In two parts

Fingers and Thumbs

In guitar music with two parts, the notes played with your fingers are shown with stems pointing upwards. The notes played with your thumb are underneath, with stems pointing downwards. Count each part separately. Do the rests belong to the finger or thumb part?

Mr Ease

In which bar does the finger part begin?

Salsa Study

Try tapping the rhythm of this piece on the body of your guitar, using your thumb and fingers as indicated by the two parts in the music.

Havana Good Time

The syncopated rhythm of bar 1 is used a lot in salsa music.
Could you make up your own tune using this rhythm?

Heart Strings

Sakura

This is a traditional Japanese melody. Try playing each part separately. You could even practise it as a duet with a friend before playing both parts yourself.

Home Sweet Home

The thumb doesn't always have the accompanying part, it can play the melody too!

Spanish Knights

Remember that *D.S. al Fine* means go back to the sign 𝄋, then play until *Fine*.

15 Way Down South

16 It's So Calypso Good

unit 4 Even higher notes

Just like low notes, high notes are written on ledger lines too.
Here are all the notes on the High E string, up to fret 12.
Practise playing up and down before you try the next three pieces.

One Finger Samba

The high version of this piece is written underneath, using numbers. The first
note is at fret 12, an **octave** or eight notes higher than open E. Follow the
numbers to find the rest of the notes. They are all played on the High E string.

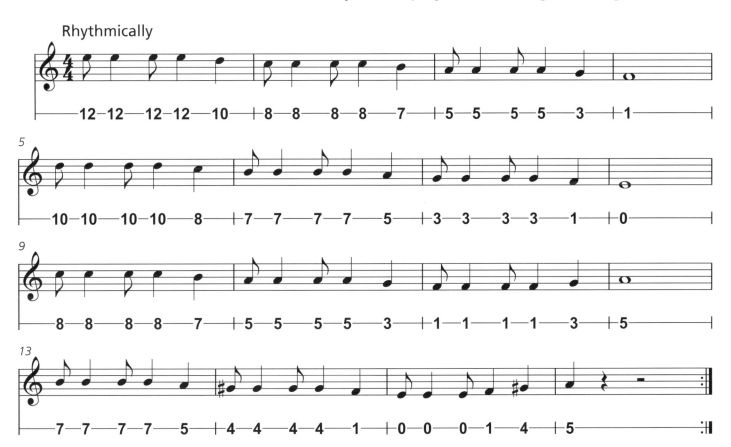

⓲ The Wackiest Racers

track

Before playing this piece, practise sliding up the E string to frets 7 and 12 with your third finger. When you're confident, try the slide with your eyes closed. Look back at the note reminder on page 4 before playing the Racer's part of the duet.

Try playing bars 9 to 11 of the Racer's part on the Low E string.
Start by sliding up to the 10th fret.

Before playing the next piece, practise this right-hand pattern.
Where can you find this rhythm in Fez'd and Furious?

Fez'd and Furious

unit 5 Arpeggios and plucked chords

You have already learnt how to strum chords (for a reminder, see Stage 15 of *Guitar Basics*) but they can also be plucked, using two fingers together. Rest your thumb (p) on the 6th string and pluck the two strings together using your index (i) and middle (m) fingers.

fact file
If you pluck the strings one at a time (as in bar 9), this is a **broken chord** or **arpeggio**. **Tirando** or 'free-stroke' means plucking into the air.

Tirando Time

Falling Leaves

You learnt the melody of this piece on page 19 of *Guitar Basics*. Now you can play the accompaniment using arpeggios. Play along with the backing track or as a duet with your teacher or a friend.

Gently

Connor's Reel

Part 2 of this duet mixes arpeggios and two-note chords.

Play this exercise by placing the three fingers of the right hand on
the three plastic strings: i on G, m on B and a (fourth finger) on E.
Don't forget to play Tirando (free-stroke).

Stand By Who?

Red Rag

My Heart Will Go On Theme from 'Titanic'

Music by James Horner   Lyric by Will Jennings

Now you can play the accompaniment to the melody above,
using a mixture of two-note chords and arpeggios.

When you see this marking ⌐———— allow the note to ring on.

unit 6 More two-part pieces

Repeat each section of the exercise below several times before you move onto the next. Always start by placing your fingers on the strings before you play the notes. Can you make the notes played by the thumb and fingers sound at exactly the same time?

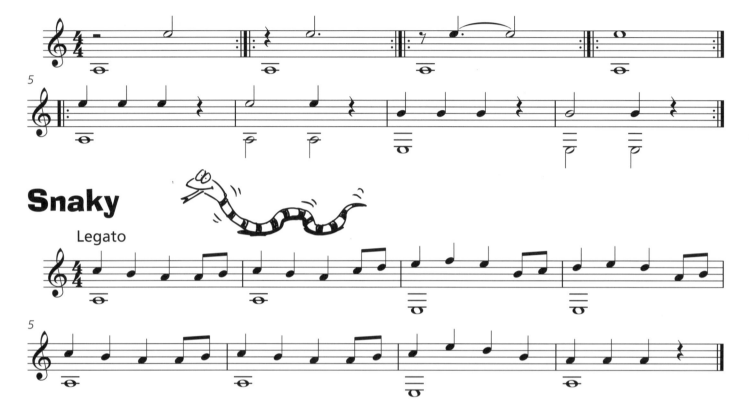

Snaky

Legato

Tudor Dance

This piece is written in the style of a 16th-century English dance. What else do you know about the Tudor period?

The two pieces on this page can be played together as a duet.

Samurai Sword

With energy

Shogun

With energy

fact file

If you move your left hand so that finger 2 (m) is at the 2nd fret,
you can reach fret 5 without sliding. This is called **second position**.
It works well when there are two sharps in the key signature.
Position markings are written with Roman numerals.

Windmill Song

This piece uses second position (II) at the beginning and end.

Flowing

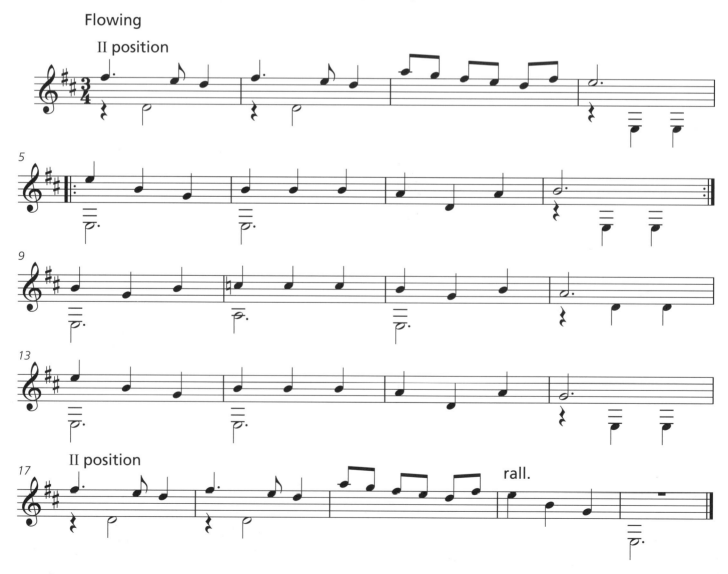

 # LemonADE

Hey Jimi!

unit 7 Concert pieces

🎵 25 Gym not P.E.

teacher's part When you get to bar 23, improvise your own melody using the notes of the C major scale while your teacher or a friend plays the accompanying chords. Then play to the end as written.

Adagio

with apologies to Erik Satie

fact file

This piece was performed by The Shadows, a British guitar group famous in the 1960s.

Apache

Music by Jerry Lordan

This piece contains triplets in bars 28 and 36, where three crotchets are played in the time of two. Practise saying and tapping this phrase before you play the piece:

Magic Study

fact file

This study will help with the unusual jumps that appear in *Hedwig's Theme*.
Notice how some of the notes seem to 'clash' – this is called **dissonance**, which
creates a mysterious mood.

Slowly

Hedwig's Theme   from 'Harry Potter and the Philosopher's Stone'

Music by John Williams

Waltz